Progressive Studies for

CLARINET

BOOK II

CHRIS ALLEN

**THE ASSOCIATED BOARD OF
THE ROYAL SCHOOLS OF MUSIC**

The aim of these studies is to provide students at all levels with instructive material, written in a modern style – slightly 'off-beat' both rhythmically and harmonically – but without abandoning formal structure.

Some of the studies are in familiar rhythms; some adopt five or seven beats in a bar; others make use of the less common groupings to be found in eight or nine beats to a bar.

Book I contains material suitable for Grades 1 to 5, and in Book II the range extends from Grade 6 to beyond Grade 8.

CHRIS ALLEN

To Colin Bradbury

PROGRESSIVE STUDIES FOR CLARINET

BOOK II

CHRIS ALLEN

36

AB 2084

4

37

Allegro molto

38

Allegretto scherzando

39

Allegretto

6

40

Moderato

41

Moto perpetuo (allegro)

42

43

decresc. poco a poco al fine

46

47

48

14

51

16

52

53

* glissando *ad lib.*   AB 2084

54

18

55

56

AB 2084

57

Andantino

58

59

22

60

Allegro con fuoco